KU-325-585

# Garfield
# takes up
# space

BY: JIM DAVIS

**BALLANTINE BOOKS · NEW YORK**

Library of Congress Catalog Card Number: 90-93221

ISBN: 0-345-37029-5

Manufactured in the United States of America

First Edition: March 1991

10   9   8   7   6   5   4   3   2   1

FROM

# Garfield's Family Album

Grandpa and a puppy that followed him home

My first refrigerator raid

Last picture of Uncle Ben

half-brother Raoul

Cousin Vi— Miss Rodent Central 1964

GARFIELD

IT TAKES YEARS OF PRACTICE TO GET THIS DEPRESSED

© 1989 United Feature Syndicate, Inc.

10-1    JIM DAVIS

ASLEEP AGAIN, GARFIELD?

DEFINE "AGAIN"

GARFIELD, HAVE YOU SEEN THE MOUSETRAP I BAITED WITH GOUDA CHEESE?

NOPE

"OOHK" "ARRRK" "EEHHK" "URRRK"

JON! OPIE! YOU'RE HOME!

HELLO, GARFIELD. HAVE SOME FOOD

GARF

JIM DAVIS 10-27

GARFIELD

LOCKED FAST WITHIN A TIME WHEN HE NO LONGER EXISTS, GARFIELD GRAPPLES WITH HIS GREATEST FEAR
... LONELINESS

© 1989 United Feature Syndicate, Inc.

AFTER YEARS OF TAKING LIFE FOR GRANTED, GARFIELD IS SHAKEN BY A HORRIFYING VISION OF THE INEVITABLE PROCESS CALLED "TIME"

HE HAS ONLY ONE WEAPON...

DENIAL...

I DON'T WANT TO BE ALONE

WANT SOME BREAKFAST, GARFIELD?

JIM DAVIS 10-28

WHO NEEDS IT? I NEED YOU!

AN IMAGINATION IS A POWERFUL TOOL. IT CAN TINT MEMORIES OF THE PAST, SHADE PERCEPTIONS OF THE PRESENT, OR PAINT A FUTURE SO VIVID THAT IT CAN ENTICE ... OR TERRIFY, ALL DEPENDING UPON HOW WE CONDUCT OURSELVES TODAY... END

© 1989 United Feature Syndicate, Inc.

THE WEATHER TODAY WILL BE PARTLY CLOUDY WITH A CHANCE OF RAIN

IF YOU NEED ME, I'LL BE OUT FRONT ROTATING THE TIRE ON MY UNICYCLE

AND THE OWNER TODAY WILL BE PARTLY DIPPY WITH A CHANCE OF STUPID

BURRRRR

RRRRRRRRP!

CLICK!

YOU'RE DISGUSTING

43 SECONDS! A NEW RECORD!

JIM DAVIS 11-15

JIM DAVIS 11-16

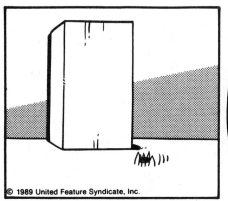

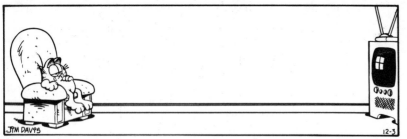

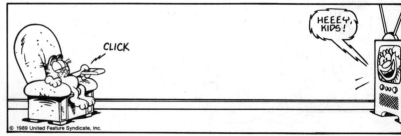

WELCOME TO "TRUTH IS STRANGER THAN FICTION THEATER"

THE FOLLOWING STORY YOU ARE ABOUT TO SEE IS ABSOLUTELY TRUE

EXCEPT, OF COURSE, FOR THE STUFF WE MADE UP TO MAKE IT MORE INTERESTING

I LOVE TELEVISION

WHAT'S NEW, GARFIELD?

1-4-90

WELL, KING KONG IS ON THE ROOF BATTING DOWN AIRPLANES. THE ENTIRE PLANET IS BEING RAVAGED BY BRAIN-EATING ALIENS...

BUT MORE IMPORTANT, MY DISH IS EMPTY

GARFIELD

JIM DAVIS

MAY I HAVE A LOCK OF YOUR HAIR?

SNIP!

I'LL KEEP IT AS A MEMENTO OF HOW STUPID YOU LOOK RIGHT NOW

2-16 JIM DAVIS

A FUNNY THING HAPPENED TO ME ON MY WAY TO THE FENCE TONIGHT

2-17

JIM DAVIS

GARFIELD®

PLASTIC BIRDBATHS REQUIRE A LESS DIRECT APPROACH

PHOOT!

PHOOT!

JIM DAVIS    2-25

IN CASE YOU DIDN'T NOTICE, I JUST CHASED A MOUSE THROUGH HERE!

BRAVO

CLAP CLAP CLAP

JIM DAVIS   3-12

ODIE AND I ARE GOING TO PLAY ON THE ROOF

ROLLER SKATES?!

LOOK OUT BELOW!

JIM DAVIS  3-13

© 1990 United Feature Syndicate, Inc.

JM DAVIS  3-25

# Ask a cat.

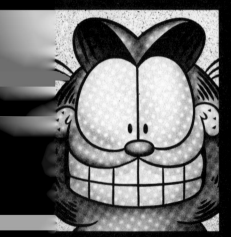

**Q:** Why does a cat always land on its feet?
**A:** Because it beats landing on its face.

**Q:** Can cats see in the dark?
**A:** Yes. They see a whole lot of dark.

**Q:** Is there more than one way to skin a cat?
**A:** I have given your name to the authorities.

**Q:** Why do cats eat plants?
**A:** To get rid of that mouse aftertaste.

**Q:** How often should I take my cat to the vet?
**A:** As often as you would like to have your lips ripped off.

**Q:** Should I have my cat fixed?
**A:** Why? Is it broken?

**Q:** Why do cats spend so much time napping?
**A:** To rest up for bedtime.

**Q:** How much food should my cat eat?
**A:** How much have you got?